Children in Medicine

Children in Medicine
Muriel Farr

Illustrated by
Elinor Jaeger

PRENTICE-HALL, INC., ENGLEWOOD CLIFFS, N. J.

PRENTICE-HALL INTERNATIONAL, INC., *London*
PRENTICE-HALL OF AUSTRALIA, PTY., LTD., *Sydney*
PRENTICE-HALL OF CANADA, LTD., *Toronto*
PRENTICE-HALL OF INDIA (PRIVATE) LTD., *New Delhi*
PRENTICE-HALL OF JAPAN, INC., *Tokyo*
PRENTICE-HALL DE MEXICO, S.A., *Mexico City*

U. S1349044

for my Mother

Contents

1.

Why British Sailors Are Called Limeys

James Cook was tired, hot and dusty. As he sat in the shadow of a hedge to rest he wondered if he could ever walk the last mile of his journey. One more mile going meant another mile coming back, besides a beating to look forward to at bedtime for being late. Was it worth it, just to look at the sea?

James was thirteen years old. He had worked hard in the Yorkshire potato fields since he was five. A month ago his father had apprenticed him to a merchant, a harsh man who gave him many beatings. James often thought of running away. But where could he go?

Reprinted, with permission, from *Public Health Nursing*, August 1952.

The most exciting thing in James' life had been a sailor's visit to the merchant's shop. The sailor had told him such wonderful tales of ships and the sea that James had decided to walk to the coast on his first free day to get a look for himself.

As he sat wondering whether to go on or to turn back, he heard the clop-clop of horses' hoofs, and a merry voice singing: "Bring out your pots and pans for old Tom the Tinker."

A shaggy pony was pulling a cart hung around with pots and pans of all descriptions. The driver was a cheery, sunburned man. As James moved to get a better look, the tinker caught sight of him.

"Hi there, boy, want a ride to Whitby? I'm a lonesome sort of cove, and like company," he called.

"Will you be going near the water, sir?" James asked.

"Right to the waterside. I have pots and pans here for His Majesty's ships. Not shipping as a cabin boy, are you? It's a hard life they say. Shouldn't want it for my son."

James climbed onto the cart. The tinker's words made him thoughtful. Was that all there was to going to sea—just going to the port and asking for a job as a cabin boy? The old sailor did say that they never could get enough boys because of the hard work and the beatings. But what had James' life ever been but hard work and beatings?

Soon James heard a deep booming noise. "Is that thunder?" he asked. "The sky looks clear."

"Thunder of the sea, not of the sky," laughed the tinker, and added, "It's easy to tell you're a land-lubber."

James was so excited he nearly fell off the cart in an effort to take in everything. The masts of the ships riding at anchor, the shrill cries of the gulls, and the smell of the tar, convinced him that here was where he belonged.

That evening the merchant would shout for James, and threaten him with a beating for hiding, and another for being late. But James would never get the beating. He had run away to sea.

James found the life of a cabin boy harder than that of a farm boy—even harder than that of an apprentice. He had little to eat. The food was salty, and often spoiled. The sleeping quarters were crowded and dirty. But James was happy. He was a born sailor and he never deserted the sea, becoming one of the greatest navigators of all time.

His first ship was a grimy coal barge which took coal from England to the northern European countries. He listened to the tales that the old sailors told: tales of the South Seas, and of strange animals: of brilliant flowers, and of fruits, which had never been seen in England. He learned anything and everything the older men offered to teach him: mathematics, astronomy, geography. Soon he rose from cabin boy to deck hand, advancing step by step to become the Master of his own ship.

Two hundred years ago the dangers of a seafaring life were great. Pirates roamed the seas, ready to seize any ship with a valuable cargo. Many sailors lost their lives or were taken as prisoners. The ships were small and many were wrecked on reefs or by storms.

But there was one danger greater than all of these put together—*scurvy*. On long voyages this dread disease killed sailors at the rate of one or more a day. First the stricken men noticed that their gums bled. Then they lost their teeth. Some had a rash, others had a painful swelling of their wrists and ankles. Finally the exhausted men became delirious and died.

James Cook noticed that the longer a voyage took, the more cases of scurvy there were. Scurvy claimed so many victims that ships often had to turn back before they reached their destinations. A sailing vessel from England took one, or possibly two, years to sail around the Pacific. Most of the expeditions that had set out to charter the South Seas had been forced to turn back because so many of the crew had died of scurvy.

In 1768, when James Cook was forty-one years old, he was appointed to conduct an expedition to the South Seas. This was his great opportunity. He must not fail as others had before him—but to succeed he had to conquer scurvy.

He had read a "Treatise on Scurvy," written by James Lind who thought that fresh fruits and vegetables had something to do with both the prevention and the cure of scurvy. This had never been proved, but Cook took aboard as many fruits and vegetables as possible. He also insisted upon absolute cleanliness and plenty of fresh air in the sailors' quarters.

His ship, *Endeavour*, was away for over two years. In his account, "The Voyages of Captain Cook," he made careful notes about every place the ship made port. Fresh fruits and vegetables were taken on whenever possible. A record of every case of scurvy was kept.

Cook did not leave a note telling when he got the idea that freedom from scurvy had more to do with the *amount* of fresh fruit and vegetables the sailors ate than with cleanliness, but he did come to this conclusion.

He had been at sea one year before scurvy appeared on his ship. It was after a long period during which the ship was unable to get fruits. This was by far the best record of any ship in the Royal Navy. Cook's interest in fresh fruit was shown by such entries as these:

"Limes. These were excellent and to be bought at twelve pence per hundred."

"Oranges. These were very good, but while we were here sold for six pence a piece."

On his second voyage Cook had an even better record. He undertook to charter the Southern globe—at least as much of it as was known in his day. Again Cook kept a careful record of everything, even describing the plants and animals that he saw. His description of a kangaroo caused great excitement, since until then no one had known such an animal existed.

The voyage lasted three years. Only one man out of a crew of 118 fell victim to scurvy and died. Others before James Cook had thought that fresh fruit prevented scurvy, but the credit for actually *proving* this to be the truth goes to Cook.

He wrote a paper on the prevention of scurvy, and was given the Copley Gold Medal for the best experimental paper of the year. The Admiralty raised him to the rank of Captain. In 1795, it became a law in the British Navy to give each man a daily ration of fruit juice.

Since lime was the fruit most commonly used, the British sailors were nicknamed "Limeys" by the sailors of other countries. The section of London called Lime-house also got its name from the days when fruit for the ships was stored in that neighborhood, close to the water-front.

When Louis Pasteur and Robert Koch discovered germs, many years later, many people thought that germs were the cause of all ills. Still later, it was discovered that there were some people who, like the sailors, became ill and died even though there were no germs in their blood or bodies.

Why were they ill? Gradually, it was found that there were substances in food needed for good health, which were missing in their bodies. A man could get enough to eat to prevent his being hungry and yet fall ill. Another, who ate less food, but a better variety, kept well. By experiments, it was discovered that certain substances must be eaten for good health. The discoverers named these substances "amines" then added *vita,* which means *life.*

Captain Cook's careful observations on the value of fresh fruit in the prevention of scurvy was the first practical use of vitamins as we know them today.

2.

Medicine and Music

Leopold Auenbrugger sat very quietly on the top step of the stairs. The big clock in the inn yard had just struck nine. It was 1731 and Leopold was nine years old. He wondered what he would be doing on his nineteenth birthday, or on his twenty-ninth.

"Are you ready, Leopold?" called a deep voice.

"Coming, Father." With a bounce, Leopold was off down the stairs as quickly as his legs would carry him. His father waited by the door with a lantern in his hand. As they went along the dark passage to the wine cellar, cobwebs brushed across their faces, and the musty smell of wine made their noses tingle.

The innkeeper placed his lantern carefully in the middle of the floor, took a piece of chalk, and went over to a large wooden cask.

"All right, Leopold, you listen and tell me where you think it is today."

Leopold stood and listened attentively while his father tapped the cask with his knuckles, from the top down towards the floor. At first the note was musical and low. Then it became flat.

"Mark it there," said Leopold, hearing the flat note.

His father took the chalk, put a mark and the date, and erased the old chalk mark above it.

Leopold and his father did this to every cask. It was a game that Leopold liked. For the innkeeper it was no game, but real business. The dull flat note told him the level of the wine in the casks. When he struck above the level of the wine, the air in the cask sounded a musical note. This way he could tell to the inch where the wine was in each—without opening the casks' heavy lids.

As soon as he was tall enough, Leopold could do the tapping by himself. Sounds had always interested him, and he had long since decided to become a musician.

There was another game of sounds that he learned from his mother. One day he noticed her tapping plates and mugs before she set them on the table.

"Why do you do that?" he asked. "There is no wine in them, and even if there were, you could see it easily."

"I tap to see if they are cracked," she answered. "A fine thing it would be to fill a plate with hot soup, and have a crack let the soup spill into a guest's lap."

Soon Leopold took over this task, too. He found that a whole plate had a clear bell-like sound, but a cracked one (even with a crack too small to be seen) had a dull broken sound.

As he grew older, Leopold kept his interest in music and in the world of sound, but he decided to study medicine as his life work, and to keep music as his hobby. He even thought of writing an opera when his medical studies were finished.

It did not take him long to discover that there are as many musical sounds in the body as there were at the inn. He was interested in the fact that the chest of a healthy person, when tapped, made a clear sound. But sometimes when he tapped the chest of a sick person, the sound was dull and flat. Many of his patients were ill and dying from all sorts of chest troubles, but because the chest is enclosed in a bony sort of box, Leopold could not tell from feeling what was wrong inside. And in Dr. Auenbrugger's day, there was no X ray to help him find out.

Then the young doctor remembered his father's wine casks, and the way he had tapped them as a child. Wasn't the chest shaped rather like a wine cask? Like the cask, it contained some air and some fluid. If he could tell from tapping a cask how much air there was in it, why couldn't he tell the same thing about a man's chest?

Leopold found that a chest filled with too much fluid, as in a person with pneumonia, made a dull flat sound when tapped. But there was more than air and fluid in a chest. He had seen the chests of persons who had died of tuberculosis. They had cavities or holes in them. Didn't he tap his mother's plates to see if they were cracked or whole? Why not tap a chest for the same reason?

Dr. Auenbrugger forgot the opera he was going to write, and wrote a book on the musical study of the chest instead. He watched sick people, tapped their chests, and learned what each sound meant. In 1761, he published a book called: *The New Invention Which Enables the Physician from Percussion of the Human Chest to Detect the Diseases Hidden Therein.*

Today, two hundred years later, doctors still use Dr. Auenbrugger's method of tapping a patient's chest when they make a physical examination. They still call one sound they hear when they tap a chest a "cracked-pot" sound. If Leopold Auenbrugger had not been such an

21

observant child, he might not have made the discoveries about the chest he did when he was a doctor.

Nearly sixty years after the birth of the innkeeper's son in Austria, another little boy was born in Brittany—Rene Theophile Hyacinthe Laënnac. This little boy also became a doctor. And he, too, was most interested in diseases of the chest, but for a different reason. His mother had died of tuberculosis.

One of the first books Laënnac studied in medical school was the one written by Dr. Auenbrugger. The hospital where he later was appointed physician was filled with soldiers suffering from tuberculosis. These soldiers of France, Dr. Laënnac's country, had been fighting the soldiers of Austria, Dr. Auenbrugger's country. The physician of one country, who had studied the book written by a physician of an enemy country, then gave priceless information to the whole world.

Dr. Laënnac studied hard. Soon he was able to tell as much about the lungs as Dr. Auenbrugger had. But there was more in a chest than lungs. What about the heart, he asked. Did it make a different sound when it was diseased? And how could a doctor hear this sound?

It is true that in 1817 a doctor had written a book in which he explained that if a physician put his ear to a

patient's chest he could hear the heart's sounds. But the sounds were muffled and not clear even in a thin person, and if the patient were fat it was often impossible to hear any sound at all.

There must be a way, he thought, to study the chest more thoroughly. Dr. Laënnac was puzzling over this problem when he stopped to watch some children playing in the gardens of the Louvre. One child placed his ear to a plank, while another scratched the other end. Dr. Laënnac watched the children for some time, wondering what the game was. At last he became so curious that he went up to a little girl.

"What are you playing," he asked her. "I don't remember playing anything like that when I was a child."

"I won't tell you," she answered with a mischievous smile. "But I'll let you play and you'll be surprised. Put your ear here and listen."

Dr. Laënnac put his ear on the plank. The little girl scratched the other end. He *was* surprised. The wood carried the sound, greatly magnified, from one end of the plank to the other. Dr. Laënnac suddenly saw the answer to his problem.

He hurried back to the hospital where he had a very ill patient suffering from heart disease, so fat a patient that Dr. Laënnac had been unable to hear any heart sounds at all. He quickly ripped the stiff covers from a book and made a cylinder of it. He placed one end of the cylinder to the patient's chest and the other to his own ear. It was one of the most exciting moments of his life. Not only could he hear heart sounds more clearly than he had ever heard them before, but he even heard the sound of air being sucked in and out of the lungs.

Dr. Laënnac began to experiment, placing little wooden trumpets on a lathe. These carried the sounds better than the paper cylinders he had first used. It was many years before the rubber tube with two ear pieces, such as doctors use today, was invented. But the principle and the name of this instrument was Dr. Laënnac's own invention. He called it a *stethoscope,* which comes from two Greek words meaning "the breast" and "to examine."

The doctor of today carries his stethoscope either hanging around his neck, or in his pocket. In the days of Dr. Laënnac's wooden cylinders, however, the doctors wore top hats, and they carried their stethoscopes in their hats.

3.

James' Brave Deed

James Phipps stood alone at his garden gate. He could still hear the words the other boys had shouted at him as they walked away:

> Cowardy, cowardy custard
> Should eat his mother's mustard.

What made it worse was that he could see his friend, Dr. Edward Jenner, passing the boys in his buggy. He must have heard what they were saying. What would he think?

"Whoa, Nellie!" bellowed the doctor. "Want to come on my rounds with me, James? I was on my way to get you."

By permission of Highlights for Children, Inc., Columbus, Ohio, copyright 1947.

The horse stopped obediently, right in front of the boy. James quickly climbed up beside his friend.

"Please let me show him that I am brave—somehow," he prayed to himself.

They drove along the English country lane in silence for a while. Then Dr. Jenner turned and asked, "Where's your tongue, James? And why no smile? Not worried because you had a fuss with your pals, are you?"

"Oh, Dr. Jenner, they say I'm a coward because I wouldn't climb over the fence into the pasture with the bull. They'd teased him so much that he was wild, and I was afraid."

He waited anxiously for the doctor's reply.

"Any sensible person is afraid of something that is dangerous. That's not cowardly, it is only being careful. If you refused to do something you *had* to do because you were afraid, that would be cowardly."

James looked puzzled, so Dr. Jenner continued, "I am afraid of some contagious illnesses, but because the people who have those diseases need my help, I go near them. I am careful, however. *You* are not a doctor and cannot cure sick people, so it would be sensible, *not cowardly*, for you to stay out of their way."

James nodded. Now he understood. "If I can ever help, you will tell me, won't you?"

"Maybe you can help me today," replied Dr. Jenner.

Before James had a chance to ask what he meant, the doctor pulled Nellie to a halt. "Here we are. Hitch Nellie to a tree, son. Then come on in."

As James tied the horse, his heart was beating fast. Now he hoped he'd have enough courage to do whatever it was that the doctor needed!

"Come in, James. You know Mistress Nelmes, don't you?"

"Yes. She milks our cows sometimes," said James as he followed the doctor into the milkmaid's cottage.

"Have you hurt your hand?" he asked Sarah Nelmes when he saw her bandage.

"No, I just have cowpox. We milkmaids often catch it from the cows. We don't mind that. You see once we have had cowpox we *never* catch *smallpox*."

"You don't look ill," James said in surprise. "I remember last year when nearly everybody in the village had smallpox," he continued. "They were dreadfully ill. Then when they got better, they had deep face scars."

"But none of the milkmaids who had had cowpox were very ill when they had it, and none were scarred," added the doctor.

"Then why don't you give everybody cowpox, so nobody would have smallpox anymore?" asked James.

Sarah Nelmes smiled. "You're a clever boy. That's just what the doctor wants to do. But you don't catch cowpox by being near it, as you do measles. You've got to get some of the fluid from the sores of the cows right under your skin."

James giggled. "Wouldn't it look funny to lead a cow down the street, and tell everybody to scratch his own hand and then touch the cow?"

"That's why I need a brave person to help me," said the doctor. "For months, I've thought of different ways to give everybody cowpox. My old teacher, John Hunter, used to say 'Don't think, try.' But I need someone to try this on. Someone who hasn't had smallpox or cowpox."

James stood very quietly as the doctor continued. "I thought of all my friends. I knew you were brave, so I asked your mother if she would object to your helping me. She said she'd be proud to have you do it. But, mind, you must help only if you want to."

The doctor had called him brave. Now was his chance to show that this was true. James was so excited that he couldn't speak. He could only nod "yes."

"Then roll up your sleeve. This will prick a bit as I do it. I'll make small scratches, then put some of the matter from Mistress Nelmes' hand in them. After about a week you will have a sore arm, I think."

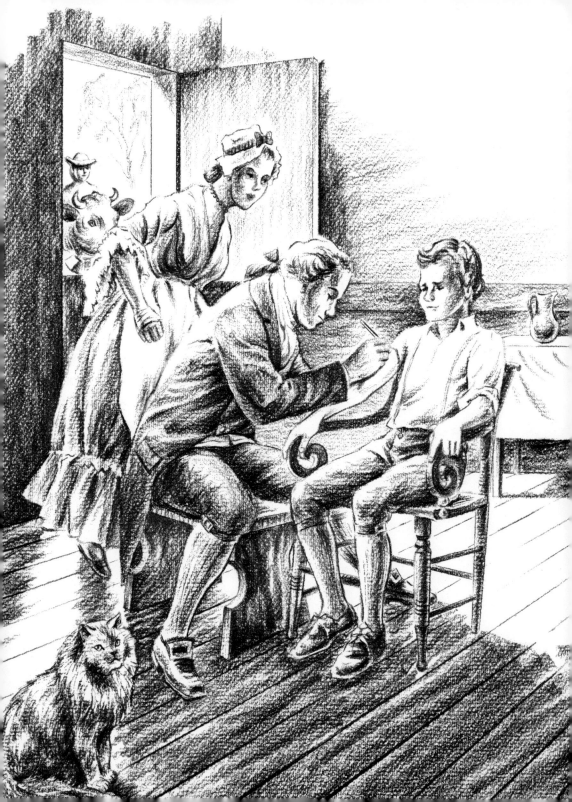

"But no worse than my hand is," said Sarah as she took off her bandages.

James held tightly to the arms of the chair as Dr. Jenner carefully vaccinated him. "Why, it did not hurt at all," he said in surprise when the doctor had finished.

"You *thought* it would so that makes you *extra* brave to have let me do it," replied the doctor. "If this really works, as I think it should, no one ever need fear smallpox again. And just wait until I see your friends, James, I'll tell them who's the bravest boy I know."

Today school children everywhere know that James' brave deed and Dr. Jenner's clever idea keep them from getting smallpox. The vaccination that they get today was discovered about 170 years ago by a clever doctor and first tested on a brave schoolboy.

4.

The Lady with the Lamp

A boy came running over the hills. It was a chilly spring morning, but he had not stopped to put on a coat. "Miss Florence, Miss Florence," he called.

Before he had time to reach the door of the big house it was opened by a little girl. "Bob, why did you run so fast? You know I'm not allowed to see the new lambs before I have had my breakfast," she said.

"That's right, she's not." The children looked up to see Sarah, the housekeeper, standing sternly in the hall. "Just because her mother and father are away doesn't mean you can take the child traipsing over the hills on an empty stomach, young man."

"Oh no, please, you don't understand. It's not the lambs, but Old Jed. He's broken his leg. Please let Miss Florence come to help."

Sarah's look softened. Everybody loved Old Jed the sheep dog. "I am sorry, Bob, but what can Miss Florence do? I know she's always doctoring sick animals, but—"

Florence interrupted. "I can help. The doctor was here last summer, and he showed me how to put a splint on. I'll finish breakfast while Bob whittles a splint."

"I knew you'd know what to do," said Bob a few minutes later, as the two children hurried to the shepherd's cottage.

They found Old Jed lying on a pile of blankets in front of the kitchen fire. He whimpered as they came in, but patiently made no sound while Florence bound on the splint with strips of cloth which the shepherd's wife tore for her.

"I do hope you can help the poor beast," said the shepherd. "We've been companions for so many years, Old Jed and I. Never a sheep has he lost. He was out all night looking for a stray. Found her, he did, but broke his leg doing it."

"I'll get Father to write to the doctor tonight," answered Florence. "He'll tell us how long to keep the splint on, and what else we should do."

34

A few weeks later, Old Jed was again searching for lost sheep. Little did anyone dream then how many more patients would owe their lives to this gifted nurse.

Florence Nightingale had been born on May 12, 1820, in the town of Florence, Italy. Her parents were English. Florence and her elder sister, Parthenope, were given a better education than was usual for young ladies of that time, and they traveled widely U. S13349044

Florence was full of energy and had a keen mind. The rather useless life of a young lady of fashion did not satisfy her. She had never given up her interest in helping the sick, and her one desire was to be a nurse. Her family was horrified. The hospitals then were not like those of today. They were dirty. Most of the nurses were ignorant and untrained. People never went to the hospital if they could find a way to be cared for at home.

In order to distract her from her purpose, Florence's family again sent her abroad. But wherever she went Florence Nightingale visited hospitals. The more she saw of the terrible conditions, the more determined she became to improve them.

Finally, in 1851, she was allowed to enter the deaconess school at Kaiserworth, Germany, where a pastor and his wife cared for the sick and taught young ladies to be nurses. The training was very sparse, but it was the best offered. After two years, she became the superintendent of an "Establishment for Gentlewomen during Illness" in London.

Just one year later the Crimean War broke out, and there were thousands of sick and wounded soldiers with no one to care for them. After one of the London newspapers told the story of the neglected men in the military hospital at Scutari, Florence Nightingale wrote to her friend, Sidney Herbert, the Secretary of War, asking to be allowed to gather together a group of nurses to go to Scutari. At the same time, Sidney Herbert had written to ask her to do that very thing. Never before had women nurses been permitted in an army hospital. Neither the doctors, nor those in charge of military operations, thought it the proper thing to do.

But on November 4, 1854, Florence Nightingale and thirty-eight women she had persuaded to help her landed in Scutari. This small band of brave women found four thousand sick and injured men awaiting them. They did not step into a well equipped hospital, as you do today. There were not enough beds. Many of the wounded were lying on dirty floors, still dressed in the muddy uniforms they had worn on the battlefields. There were no wash basins, no soap, no towels, no laundry for clothes— not even any scrubbing brushes to clean the wards.

Florence Nightingale's first thought was of cleanliness. With the help of the soldiers' wives who had followed their husbands to the front, she scrubbed the wards and established a laundry and a kitchen.

Florence Nightingale never lost hope. The effects of her work were soon appreciated by the doctors and army officials who had opposed her coming. But no one appreciated her as much as the sick themselves. This is what one wounded boy wrote home: "What a comfort it was to see her pass, even. She would speak to one and nod and smile to as many more: but she could not do it all, you know. We lay there by the hundreds, but we could kiss her shadow as it fell, and lay our heads on the pillow again, content."

Stories of her work were published in the papers while she was still in Crimea. A grateful people collected a sum of money which they donated to her when she returned to England. She accepted the money gratefully, and used it for the purpose nearest her heart—to establish a school in which to train nurses. On June 24, 1860, The Florence Nightingale School For Nurses of St. Thomas' Hospital, London, was opened, under her personal direction.

Florence Nightingale lived to be ninety years old. For almost half of her life she was an invalid, due to the privations she suffered in Crimea, and she kept her interest in nursing to the last. From her couch, she directed and helped to establish sanitary reforms all over the world.

In 1915, a memorial to the Crimean War was unveiled in London. One of the figures was "The Lady with the Lamp." Except for statues of royalty, this was the first public statue erected to a woman in London. Florence Nightingale also has a memorial in this country, but of a different kind: Her birthday, May 12, has been proclaimed "National Hospital Day."

5.

Medicine and Mad Dogs

When the weather was clear, as it was today, Jean Baptiste Jupille, the shepherd boy, could sit on the hillside and carve himself a new pair of wooden shoes, or a whistle. He knew his faithful dog would look after the sheep. When it was stormy, there was a hut to shelter both the boy and the dog from the wind and the rain. It was a good life.

Jean heard the shrill voices of children, and saw a group of boys and girls playing by the roadside. He waved. They called, "May we come with you today, Jean? There is nothing else to do." He was about to say yes, but his voice stopped in horror, and the clop of his wooden shoes quickened.

A mad dog, foaming at the mouth was springing at the children! Jean knew enough about dogs to know what this meant. He knew the bite of a mad dog could kill. The maddened animal's brain, damaged by illness, knew no reason, and made it attack friends as well as strangers.

Without hesitation, Jean brandished his whip and rushed to help the children. The dog caught Jean's hand in its sharp teeth. The children stood still, too terrified to move. Jean shouted to them to run for help. He struggled to throw the maddened animal to the ground. Then with his whip and his free hand, he pried the animal's jaws apart and loosened his torn hand.

Although the dog bit him several times, Jean did not give up until he had tied the dog's jaws shut with his whip. Had he let it run wild, the animal would surely have bitten others.

The cries of the children soon brought help. One man bound up Jean's wounds, while another sent for the village priest. For did not those bitten by a mad dog always die of rabies?

The priest, however, did not send Jean home to die. He summoned a farmer and had Jean moved in a wagon to the chemist, Louis Pasteur. The priest had heard that a few weeks ago this chemist had cured a nine-year-old boy, Joseph Meister, who had been bitten fourteen times

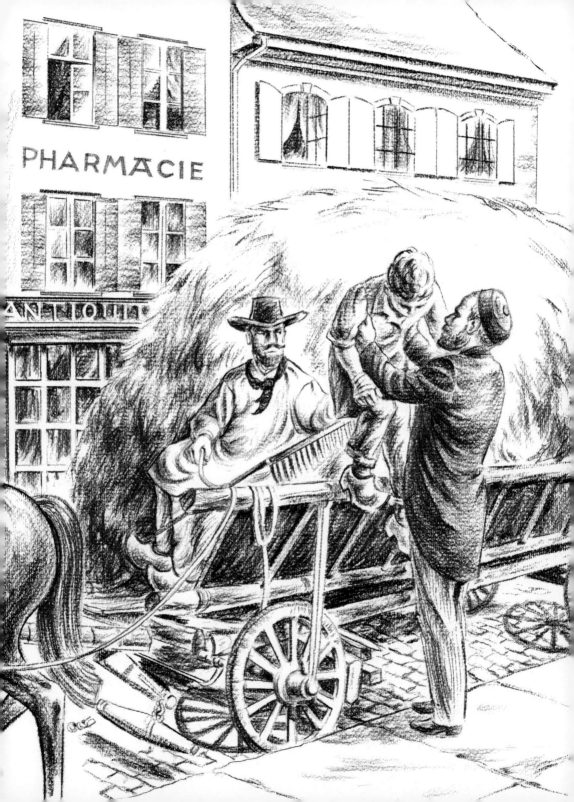

by a mad dog, and Louis Pasteur, the chemist, cured Jean, too.

Louis Pasteur, who discovered the cure for rabies, was born December, 1822, in the town of Dole, France. He was the first to prove that diseases were caused and spread by animals too small to be seen by the naked eye. As they could only be seen through a microscope, they were named microorganisms, more commonly known as germs.

When Pasteur discovered these microorganisms he was not looking for the cause of human ills at all. He was a chemist, not a doctor, and was searching for the cause of fermentation in wines. He lived in the grape-growing area of France, and many of his neighbors had been ruined when their wines spoiled. Pasteur proved that the wines spoiled because something dropped into them from the air. Ten years later, he investigated the diseases of silkworms. During the next twelve years, he studied the diseases of beer and of chickens. In all of these studies, he discovered that the changes were due to small organisms that exist in the air.

Pasteur began to wonder if microorganisms might not also cause diseases in human beings. He published a pamphlet stating that germs are all about us in the air, and that when they enter the body they cause disease.

If all diseases were caused by germs, Pasteur reasoned, rabies must also be caused by a germ. Rabies caused havoc in the farm areas. When a rabid dog bit cattle, other dogs, men, women and children—nearly all died. There was no cure or prevention known.

Louis Pasteur experimented with the rabies germ from 1881 until 1885. First he proved that the germ could be found in the saliva of a dog's mouth. When the sick dog bit anyone, the poison spread from the bite to the brain, causing madness in both the human and the animal. The next step was to prove that if the saliva of the mad animal was injected into the brain of a healthy animal it, too, would cause madness. Then Pasteur wondered: If he could cause illness, could he cure it?

He began his rabies experiments by injecting a weak solution of the *virus* (infected material) too small to cause illness, into dogs, following it with more doses, each one stronger than the last. These animals, along with an equal number who had received no injections, were put into a cage with a mad dog. The dogs who had been injected did not become ill from the bites. And every one of the non-injected dogs sickened.

It was at this point that Joseph Meister had been brought to Pasteur. The child was so severely bitten that, without treatment, he would surely have died. Pasteur had never tried his experiments on a human being. Besides, he was a chemist, not a doctor. A group of physicians was asked for its opinion. Should Pasteur inoculate the boy as he had the dogs? The physicians agreed that he should.

On July 6, 1885, at six o'clock in the evening, sixty hours after he had been bitten, Joseph was given his first injection. Each day until July 16 he was given another injection of increasing strength. It was on this day that Pasteur proved his cure: He injected his strongest solution of rabies poison into Joseph—an amount strong enough to kill a grown man. Joseph lived.

The next patient brought to Pasteur was the brave Jean. The recovery of these two boys showed that with the proper precautions no one need die of rabies again. Today puppies are injected so that they will not develop rabies, and should a person be bitten by a rabid animal he can also be protected.

Today if you go to the yard of the Pasteur Institute in Paris you will see one of the few statues erected to a child. It is the statue of a heroic shepherd boy, Jean Baptiste Jupille, struggling with a mad dog.

6.

Donald's Day at the Fair

"Donald, hurry now, or ye'll be late for the fair," called his father.

Donald hurried. Within a very short time, he and his father had joined the noisy crowd headed for the Glasgow Fair. The streets were gaily decorated with red, white and blue streamers. Scottish flags and Union Jacks waved merrily in the breeze. Donald was so busy looking around that he would have gone right past the entrance to the fair grounds if his father had not pulled him back.

"Pay heed, lad. Dreaming will cause you trouble this day. Keep your eyes and ears open. There are wonderful things to see and hear. Why, they've even put a cable thing across to America. Right under the sea it is. Men can send messages three thousand miles in a few hours. And this very morning Tad was telling me of a young doctor who has discovered how to stop blood poisoning. Joseph Lister I think his name is.

"But what am I rambling on for? Today is for fun. Here!" He handed Donald some money. "Spend this how you like. Meet me at the gate at noon. We'll eat while resting, and be fresh for the pony auction this afternoon."

Donald looked at the money in his hand. Then his father's words struck him suddenly. He forgot the money. His father had as much as said that he would buy Donald a pony!

He ran to the pony enclosure. It would be well to look the ponies over so he would know which one to bid on later. As he leaned on the fence, three ponies came and sniffed at him in a friendly way. One was white, one spotted gray, and the other a warm brown color.

"Oh, I hope the brown one will like me," he wished to himself. He held out his hand. "Come on, I won't hurt you," he said softly.

With a toss of his head, the white pony turned and trotted away, followed by the spotted one. But the little brown pony came right up to Donald, let himself be petted and nuzzled closer.

48

"Like him, son, do you?"

Donald looked up to see who was speaking. He had been so busy making friends with the pony that he had forgotten where he was. It was the owner of the ponies. "He's a good one," the owner continued. "You come around when the bidding starts, if you want him. Tell your dad to bid on Tom."

The mention of his father made Donald realize that he should be at the gate this very minute to meet him. As he ran, he wondered what the other boys at school would trade him for a ride on his pony. Bob might lend him his fishing rod. Mac would give him one of his mother's good cookies. . . .

A loud whirring noise interrupted Donald's dreaming. He swung around quickly, but he was too late. He had run into a farm machine. Before he could pull away, his arm was caught fast. He screamed for his father.

Someone stopped the machine, freeing his arm. Donald heard a voice saying "Take him to the Glasgow Infirmary. That's where Dr. Lister is, you know."

Before he lost consciousness, Donald managed to say: "Tell Dad to bid on Tom."

When Donald awoke, he found himself in bed. There was a queer smell somewhere nearby. His arm hurt badly. He moaned.

"It is all right now, my boy," said a kindly voice. "Your arm will hurt a bit until it heals, but that will not be long."

Donald felt a gentle hand wiping the hair away from his damp forehead. The queer smell seemed to be coming from that hand. Donald opened his eyes to see who it was sitting beside him. He saw a friendly young man who was a stranger to him.

"Who are you? How do you know my arm will heal," he asked. "What is that smell? Where is my father?"

"One question at a time, please. I am Dr. Lister, your father said he told you about me this morning. The smell is carbolic. I washed your arm and my hands with it. That is why I am sure your arm will heal. I have found that if wounds are washed with carbolic, they will heal without becoming infected."

Then the doctor added something that Donald *really* wanted to hear: "Your father told me to tell you that he was not here because he had gone to do business with a man about a pony called Tom."

Donald's arm did heal without infection. That is why we know about him today. For less than one hundred years ago, even the most famous surgeons did not know what every child knows today—that wounds should be washed or they will become infected. No one likes the

sting of putting soap and water and a disinfectant on a cut. But everyone knows it must be done.

Before Dr. Lister discovered that carbolic used as a wash on a wound, on a surgeon's hands and on the instruments he was using, would prevent infection, everyone thought that infection was a normal part of healing.

Dr. Lister himself discovered *why* open wounds become infected after reading a pamphlet published by Louis Pasteur, a French chemist, stating that germs are all about us in the air, and that when they are permitted to enter the body, they cause infection.

Even when Dr. Lister read his paper on Antiseptic Surgery before a group of physicians in 1867, most of them laughed. Whoever heard of washing a wound? Whoever heard of boiling a needle and thread, used to sew up wounds?

Some doctors, however, listened. They tried Dr. Lister's ideas, and found that their patients' wounds healed without infection. They found that badly wounded legs and arms would not always have to be amputated.

When reporting on Donald, Dr. Lister himself said: "Without antiseptic treatment, I should certainly have thought of nothing but amputation at the shoulder joint."

And Donald was only the second badly wounded patient of Dr. Lister's who healed without infection. Before Dr. Lister died in 1912, he saw the results of his discovery. Doctors all over the world had learned to clean wounds, and everything that touched them. Dr. Lister was made a baron in 1883, eighteen years after he had cured Donald, the very first physician to receive such an honor. Two years after his death, thousands of men wounded on the battlefields of the first World War owed their lives to him. Millions more hurt every day in all kinds of accidents owe their lives to this kindly English Quaker physician.

7.

The Great Medical Explorer

In the little town of Klausthal, nestled in the Hartz Mountains of Germany, there lived a silver miner, Herr Koch, his wife and their thirteen children.

There was very little money while the children were small. Often their meals were nothing more than a slice of black bread and a cup of milk. The children, however, did not feel sorry for themselves. Who else had more fun? Their father told the best stories of anyone they knew. On long winter evenings he would sit by the fire smoking his pipe, and tell the smaller children fairy stories. After the younger ones had gone to bed, the older children listened with excitement to his tales of adventure and travel.

Robert, the third child, was especially fond of wandering in the woods or over the mountains. He loved listening to his father's tales, but best of all he liked discovering things for himself. He collected plants, mosses, insects and stones. Every night he had another box of treasures to add to the museum he had set up in the corner of his room.

One wet day as he was going through an old chest of his father's in the attic, Robert found a pocket lens, and was overjoyed when his father said that he might keep it. Now he could really study his collection. He could see how ants' legs worked, and how the eyes of a fly were joined to its head. He could see what a wonderful thing the inside of a seed was, and how beautiful the patterns on a leaf were.

Robert finished school at the head of his class. Luckily, he did not have to go straight to work to help support his brothers and sisters, for his father had been given a higher position in the mining company, and could afford to send his clever son to the University for at least one year.

When Robert Koch was nineteen years old (on Easter Sunday, 1862) he entered the University of Göttingen. He still kept to his old interests, the study of plants and animals, yet he had never forgotten his father's tales of

travel. Robert wished to see foreign lands for himself—
he decided to study medicine, and become a ship's doctor. In this way, he could still study living things—under a microscope now, instead of a scratched pocket lens—and get all the traveling he wished.

Herr Koch was not too pleased that his son had chosen to study medicine. Most doctors, he thought, did not know enough to cure even simple illnesses. But when Robert wrote that he had won the first prize for the investigation of a scientific study, he changed his mind, and wrote Robert of his approval—for the sum of money that he had won made it possible for him to stay on at the University until he had completed his studies.

When Dr. Koch finished his medical course he still planned to travel, but neither his mother nor the girl he wished to marry wanted him to leave home. He settled down to practice medicine in a small town on the Russian border.

Within a year the Franco-Prussian war broke out, and Dr. Koch became an army surgeon. He was placed in charge of a hospital where soldiers ill with typhoid fever were sent. This aroused his interest in communicable diseases.

In 1871, he returned from the war and set up private practice again. His first wife had died, and he remarried.

On his twenty-eighth birthday, his second wife gave him a microscope. It became one of his most treasured possessions.

Dr. Koch had always been impressed with the idea that germs caused disease. One of his teachers, Jacob Heine, had written a book about the connection between communicable diseases and microbes. Dr. Koch had also read the work of the French chemist, Louis Pasteur. The doctor was very interested in the chemist's theory that *living things* caused disease. Dr. Koch himself had seen how typhoid fever spread from one soldier to another in the crowded army camps, and he wondered if living things caused this.

Dr. Koch had no laboratory and no expensive equipment, but his childhood had taught him to make do with very little. He divided off a part of his consultation room with a curtain, bought a few ordinary utensils, and with his precious microscope he began to study these microscopic animals himself.

Dr. Koch started his experiments on a problem close at hand—*anthrax,* a highly contagious disease which was killing thousands of sheep in his district.

The young doctor examined the blood of dead sheep under his microscope and found little rod-shaped germs. Some were separate. Some stuck together in chains. He

had never seen these before. They were not found in the blood of healthy animals. Were they the cause of the disease? Dr. Koch did not permit himself to wonder. He began to search for proof. He injected the blood from sick sheep into healthy white mice. The mice died. When he examined the blood of the dead mice, Dr. Koch found the same rods which had been present in the blood of the sick sheep.

He noticed another strange thing. When he examined the blood before he injected it, and then examined the blood of the dead mice, he found that there were more rods in the blood of the dead mice than he had injected into them. This proved that germs grow and multiply in the living animal.

If germs lived and multiplied inside a body could they grow and multiply outside of a body? If so, Dr. Koch thought, here was a way to study how a disease spread once it had infected a person. This might also show how the disease spread from one person to another.

Both Joseph Lister and Louis Pasteur believed that the air was full of living things which caused disease when they dropped into an open wound. Dr. Koch set out to prove, or disprove this belief.

He put some anthrax germs in fluid and watched them grow under the microscope. Then he proved that germs grown *outside* the body are just as deadly as those grown *inside*. He injected an animal with the germs he had grown in fluid and found that they killed just as fast as those grown inside a body.

Here was the one great fact that explained the spread of disease. It explained why open wounds, if unwashed, became infected by germs in the air. It explained how Dr. Lister killed germs with carbolic *before they had a chance to grow*. Lastly, Dr. Koch's discovery explained how measles spread in a classroom, and how children got diphtheria, mumps and chicken pox from germs that grew *outside of their bodies*.

In 1905, Dr. Koch was awarded the Nobel prize for his work with germs. Shortly afterward, he set off on his last journey to study sleeping sickness in Africa. Although he never sailed abroad as a ship's doctor, he spent his whole life in exploration: First as a little boy in the forests and mountains near his home; next as a young man in the world of microscopes and germs; later as a research doctor in Egypt and India studying Asiatic Cholera; then in South Africa investigating cattle pests, and lastly in Africa studying tropical diseases. Truly, Dr. Robert Koch was a great medical explorer.

8.

The Woodsman Physician

Edward Trudeau lit the fuse of the cannon on his boat and headed it directly toward the enemy vessel. The cannon went off with a loud explosion, rocking all the boats in the basin of the fountain of the Tuileries Gardens in Paris. But, as usual, the only boat that overturned was not an enemy one. There was a great cheer from the enemy, and a loud groan from Edward's brother and his friends.

Edward pulled his boat in with a long stick. It was a beautiful model, and its sails and rigging glistened in the sun. He lifted the cannon off the deck, took something from his pocket and fastened this to the end of the bowsprit.

"What are you doing now?" asked his brother. "You know that you never steer that boat of yours straight. Give it to me. I bet I can sink all those Confederates."

"No, wait," said Edward as he gave his boat a hard shove toward the nearest enemy ship. This time the boat rammed one of the enemy boats, tearing her sails.

"See," called Edward, holding up the victorious ship. Enemies and friends gathered around to see what the lethal weapon had been. It was a sharpened steel ink eraser.

Edward and his friends were all American—some from the North and some from the South. All of them were living in Paris, France, during the time of the Civil War.

Edward Trudeau had been born October 5, 1848, in New York. When he was three years old, he and his older brother had gone to live with their grandparents in Paris. They stayed there nearly fifteen years. When they returned to the United States, they practically had to learn to speak English all over again.

As he grew older Edward had a hard time deciding what he wanted to do in life. He and his brother had been taught to love the outdoors by their father who was a physician by profession but who spent all of his spare time in the woods. He had once spent two years with the Osage Indians. Very few children knew as much of

Indian lore, and of the ways of woodsmen, as did the Trudeau brothers. Not only did their father know Indian ways, but he was a friend of John J. Audubon, and went with the naturalist on many of his expeditions, often drawing bird and egg illustrations for him.

With this love of the outdoors, combined with his childhood interest in ships and the sea, is it any wonder that Edward finally decided to be a sailor? He applied for an appointment to the Naval Academy, and was jubilant when he received it.

But before he embarked upon his career, something happened to change his whole life. His older brother, of whom he was very fond, became ill with tuberculosis. Edward gave up his appointment to the Naval Academy, and went to his grandfather's house to nurse his brother. At that time, there was no known cure for this disease. Nor was it known that it was communicable. Edward knew his brother would never recover. Trudeau later said in his autobiography: "We occupied the same room and sometimes the same bed. . . . I tried to cheer him through the long days of fever and sickness." Trudeau also said that the doctor told him never to open a window as it might make his brother's cough worse.

When Edward was seventeen, his brother died. All thoughts of a naval career left him, and he was more undecided than ever what to do. Even though his father and his mother's father were physicians, until he nursed his brother he had never thought of entering the medical profession himself. In 1868, Edward Trudeau entered the College of Physicians and Surgeons in New York. His work in the years after was a tribute to his brother, but he had more than the memory of his brother to make him work hard. He was in love. He knew that before he could marry he had to be able to make a living.

Three years later, Dr. Edward Trudeau and Charlotte Beare were married. A year later, Dr. Trudeau became the partner of a prominent New York doctor. He was tired all the time, but thought nothing of it. He was working hard enough to be tired.

The fatigue, however, got worse. A medical examination showed that he had tuberculosis. All dreams of a useful, happy life were shattered. He remembered his brother, and thought that he would only have a little time to live. He felt that he could not live that little time in crowded New York City, but must be out in the open, in the woods that he and his father loved so well.

The fresh air did not make Dr. Trudeau's cough worse, as the doctors had feared, but improved it. In four months, Dr. Trudeau returned to New York. He had lost his fever, had a good appetite, and had gained fifteen pounds. He thought he was cured, but within a short time he was ill again, and returned to the Adirondacks. Even though it was winter, his wife and children went with him.

In spite of the cold, and the snow, the sick man again improved. When the summer came, he was well enough to act as the house doctor for the hotel's guests. At the close of the summer season, the Trudeaus decided to rent a house of their own at nearby Saranac Lake. They went there in 1876, and remained there for the rest of their lives.

Dr. Trudeau wrote: "How strange that after helping stifle my brother and infecting myself through such teaching that was then in vogue, I should have lived to save my own life, and that of many others, by the simple expedient of an abundance of fresh air. . . ."

The doctor who had first told Trudeau that he had tuberculosis, Dr. Alfred Loomis, was so impressed that he sent other patients with the same disease to Saranac Lake. Dr. Trudeau welcomed the company of fellow patients and tried to help them.

One day Dr. Trudeau read of Brehmer's Sanitorium in Silesia, in Europe. Dr. Hermann Brehmer's treatment was really what he had given himself: fresh air, rest, and good food. In 1882, Dr. Trudeau met Dr. Loomis and told him he was thinking of building a few cottages at the lake, where he could try the fresh air and rest treatment for other patients. Tuberculosis was still not considered contagious, but Dr. Trudeau thought that the sick people would like small cottages, where they could be by themselves.

All of Dr. Trudeau's friends were interested in the idea of the Sanitorium and offered to help him. When the Trudeaus went to New York that summer, Dr. Trudeau took a subscription book and collected three thousand dollars toward the cost of building his sanitorium. The first cottage was finished in 1885. It was only large enough for two patients. The first ones to use it were two factory girls sent by Dr. Loomis.

Trudeau was given a wonderful Christmas present that year—a translation of Robert Koch's work on the discovery of the tubercule bacillus. Trudeau found that most of his professors in medical school were not impressed with the importance of the discovery, but to him it was the most marvelous thing that had ever happened. He went to New York to learn how to recognize the bacillus under the microscope.

Upon his return to Saranac, he fitted up a room in one of the cottages, and with as little equipment as Koch had when he started, began his research on tuberculosis.

Trudeau, like other researchers, did not think of fame. He liked and wanted to help people. His one idea was to conquer tuberculosis. Those who knew him called him "The Beloved Physician."

Trudeau used rabbits in his experiments. He divided them into three groups. The first he inoculated with the tubercule bacilli. He gave them good light, fresh air, and good food. The second group was given the same inoculation as the first, but was put in poor light, poor air, and fed poor food. The third group was not inoculated, but was given the same poor light, air and food as the second.

Of the rabbits in the first group, all but one lived. Of those in the second group, all but one died. All of the rabbits in the third group lived. These were thin, but not having been given, or exposed to, tuberculosis, they did not develop it.

This proved to Dr. Trudeau that poor surroundings would not produce tuberculosis—but if the germs were present, bad surroundings would prevent recovery. This explained why Trudeau's treatment had cured his patients.

Soon the fame of the Sanitorium spread around the world. One of the best known and loved persons to seek treatment was Robert Louis Stevenson, the author of *Treasure Island,* and *A Child's Garden of Verses.* He was helped, but not cured, as he had been ill too long ever to be well again.

Many years have passed since that first little cottage was built. It is still standing on the shores of Saranac Lake, and is now known as the Trudeau-Saranac Laboratory. The beds in the cottages which surround it have been empty since December 1, 1954. There are no longer enough patients in that area to fill them. This does not mean that tuberculosis, today, is not a public health problem. Thousands of persons become infected with the disease each year, but their numbers are declining, and their hopes of recovery are great, thanks to the continuous research of the Trudeau-Saranac Laboratory.

P·H
JUNIOR
RESEARCH
BOOKS

explore subjects in depth—